Bar 1   In Mozart's day it was always assumed that in the absence of marks a solo player would begin a theme *poco forte* or *mezzo piano*. The latter mark (given in brackets) meets the situation here.

b.8   The all-important feature in this bar is the entry of a new voice on the G in r.h. It is hardly possible to make this clear unless l.h. takes over the last semiquaver.

b.23   Let the *piano* be sudden here and at b.125. It is poor playing and poor interpretation to let the tone drop before it, or to begin with a bump.

Learn a good staccato in the left thumb and forefinger over a well-sustained *and rhythmic* little finger:

Strange to say, this is, by the very reason of the fixed little finger, a delightful exercise for loosening the wrist. Bring out the theme in this l.h. passage, also in bb.69–84 and in the recapitulation, keeping r.h. very light.

b.150   The effect of repeating the second part is not a very evident triumph of Beethoven's imagination, the irruption of A♭ (♭III.) being characteristically violent but not quite convincing. But why not try it out and see if it convinces you? The pause applies only to the real end of the sonata, and it should not intervene at the moment of making the repeat.

DONALD FRANCIS TOVEY

Dedicated to the Countess von Browne

SONATA
in F

BEETHOVEN Op. 10 No. 2

Allegro

6

A. B. 237.

BEETHOVEN
Sonatas for Pianoforte

Phrasing and fingering by Harold Craxton

Commentaries by Donald Francis Tovey

1 F minor, Op.2 No.1
2 A major, Op.2 No.2
3 C major, Op.2 No.3
4 E flat major, Op.7
5 C minor, Op.10 No.1
6 F major, Op.10 No.2
7 D major, Op.10 No.3
8 C minor, Op.13 (*Pathétique*)
9 E major, Op.14 No.1
10 G major, Op.14 No.2
11 B flat major, Op.22
12 A flat major, Op.26
13 E flat major, Op.27 No.1
   (quasi fantasia)
14 C sharp minor, Op.27 No.2
   (quasi fantasia) (*Moonlight*)
15 D major, Op.28 (*Pastorale*)

16 G major, Op.31 No.1
17 D minor, Op.31 No.2
18 E flat major, Op.31 No.3
19 G minor, Op.49 No.1
20 G major, Op.49 No.2
21 C major, Op.53 (*Waldstein*)
22 F major, Op.54
23 F minor, Op.57 (*Appassionata*)
24 F sharp major, Op.78
25 G major, Op.79
26 E flat major, Op.81a (*Les adieux*)
27 E minor, Op.90
28 A major, Op.101
29 B flat major, Op.106 (*Hammerklavier*)
30 E major, Op.109
31 A flat major, Op.110
32 C minor, Op.111

THE ASSOCIATED BOARD OF
THE ROYAL SCHOOLS OF MUSIC

SONATA in F major, Op.10 No.2

Allegro

Like the first movement of Op.14 No.2, and the rondos in Op.7 and 22, this tempo is on a quaver standard such as is commoner in Haydn's early works than in later music, but not unlikely to recur when a style is cultivated at a ripe stage of development. The present tempo is considerably too fast for 4-in-a-bar; yet demisemiquavers are its chief mode of vibration, and semiquavers are purely melodious, needing to break into triplets before they can become mere figures of accompaniment. Take your tempo from bb.9–10.

Bars 1–3 The triplet figure is melody, not a mere twiddle. Even the dot over the crotchet should not reduce that note to a quaver.

b.5 The first semiquaver is dotted in later recurrences. This is a variation, not a discrepancy.

bb.5–8 Get a fine legato in the l.h.

bb.9–10 The 6-note shake and turn

should be easy here. In b.10 put the first grace-note on the beat and do not let it spoil the end of b.9.

bb.31–35 The *sforzandos*, though strongly marked, should not heat this passage up beyond its fundamental *piano*.

bb.38–39 The 4-note turn ♫ is best here.

b.42 The *fortissimo* is very characteristic of Beethoven's early marking. He knows as well as we do that there is not much tone to be got from this passage; but in spiritual energy there is not much to choose between kittens and tigers.

bb.46–50 A beautiful example of the difference between dashes and dots. No wonder Beethoven was anxious about it. Here we have positive evidence that these bars are not to be hard or spiky, but in contrast to 44–45.

bb.69–76 A test of steadiness and clearness of rhythm in both hands. Do not spoil the grace of b.72 and the surprise of the sudden *forte* by either the crescendo of stupid virtuosos or the hustle of players who will not practise patiently. Play b.72, with a 4-note turn ♫ as

if nothing could disturb it, and meanwhile make a mental image of the exact muscular sensation of a firmly-grasped D minor chord. Then translate that idea into action, not forcing the tone but letting it grow with confidence and experience. Stimulate this by the good *forte* you can easily get in the l.h., and keep this up all through b.76.

b.77 Note that only the outlying bass-notes are staccato. The chords should be *tenute*, like soft horns and bassoons, or strings playing with the *louré* stroke in which the bow moves in one direction, halting but not leaving the strings.

b.202 It is possible that you may have time to play this sonata to please yourself, instead of confining your view of it to that of a concert-player with an overcrowded programme and a mortal fear of those eminent critics whose knowledge of early Beethoven is confined to the statement that 'this smacks of the schoolroom'. Beethoven himself retained a special affection for this sonata long after he was out of sympathy with most of his early works. If you try the effect, you will discover that he meant something very definite by directing a repeat of the second part. The rise to the dominant of D minor is quite a new point; the whole episodic development, like Mozart's examples of the kind, seems to become more organic by repetition, and the delicious and subtle recapitulation *via* D major gives the more pleasure for the memory that makes it expected. Even with both repeats the movement will not take eight minutes.

Allegretto

Beethoven's early lyric pathos is at its height in this quiet movement. With the exception of Beethoven's long slurs in the l.h. of bb.23–24 and 27–28, which are here corrected to this model in the recapitulation in bb.155–156 & 159–160, the whole is adequately covered by the general advice to make sure that you are playing exactly what Beethoven has written. Do not neglect the normal accentuation of the first beat of each bar when there is no cross-rhythm, and do not obliterate cross-rhythm *sforzandos* by equally strong normal accents. Lastly, do not (in spite of the bad example here given in bb.23–24 & 27–28) level down the differences between first statements and their repetitions. The repeats are written out in full for the express purpose of delicate differences. Find these out for yourself and bring them out in your playing as if you meant them. If in memorising this movement you feel vague about them, you must realise that your work has only just begun, and that technical difficulty is here only a small part of the problem.

Bar 6 The grace-note is probably short, as in the Menuet of Op.2 No.1.

b.15 Note that the bass is D♭, not D♮ as in b.147.

b.42 Turn of three notes before the beat: ♫.

bb.168–169 When you have realised the pathos of the whole, you may feel offended by the *forte* end. Why not *piano*, as in bb.36–37? But when you understand *that*, you will know something worth knowing about Beethoven.

Presto

After two movements that make no demands on an advanced technique, Beethoven gives us a finale as difficult as many later things four times as large. Although the movement is extremely lively, the direction *Presto* should be followed with caution. A lively delivery should be and can be achieved at an obviously safe pace, and this should be taken as the limit until years of experience have given the player a reserve of athletic form sufficient for bigger things. A scrambling performance of this movement is among the ugliest experiences in music, and is permanently hurtful to the technique and style of the scrambler. The scrambler himself would probably have a poor opinion of the final tempo of a great player in this movement. So the young student need not be discouraged: the safe pace may prove fast enough after all.

BEETHOVEN'S PIANOFORTE SONATAS
are also available in three volumes
in either paper or cloth covers

BEETHOVEN'S SIX SONATINAS
are published complete in one volume

A COMPANION TO BEETHOVEN'S PIANOFORTE SONATAS
by Donald Francis Tovey (demy 8vo 284 pp)
gives complete bar-to-bar analyses of the sonatas

ABRSM
PUBLISHING

The Associated Board of
the Royal Schools of Music
(Publishing) Limited

14 Bedford Square
London WC1B 3JG

ISBN 1-85472-013-9

9 781854 720139